Now You Can Read Stories

WRITTEN BY
June Woodman

ILLUSTRATED BY
Pamela Storey

BRIMAX

SILLY
DILLY DUCK

Dilly Duck goes to the pond.
Her three little ducklings
go with her.
"Come with me," says Dilly.
"I will take you for a swim
in the duck pond."
But the little ducklings are
afraid. They do not want
to go to the duck pond.
"We do not know how to
swim!" they say.
But Dilly Duck does not
hear them.
Silly Dilly Duck!

Bossy Bear plays with
his roller-skates. He has
a lot of fun.
He sees Dilly Duck come
along the lane. He sees
the three little ducklings
with her.
"Where are you going?"
says Bossy Bear.
"To the duck pond," says the
first little duckling.
"But I do not want to go."

"Why not?" says Bossy Bear.
"I cannot swim," says
the first little duckling.
"We can play a trick," says
Bossy Bear.
"I will go to the duck pond.
You stay here. You can play
with my roller-skates."
The first little duckling
thinks that will be fun.
He puts on the skates.

Dilly Duck is on her way to
have a swim in the duck pond.
The two little ducklings
and Bossy Bear go along too.
But silly Dilly Duck does not
see Bossy Bear.
The two little ducklings and
Bossy Bear think that this
is very funny. Bossy Bear
likes to play funny tricks.

They all go along the lane.
Soon they meet Hoppy Rabbit.
He drives in his little car.
"Where are you going?"
says Hoppy Rabbit.
"To the duck pond," says
the second little duckling.
"But I do not want to go."
"Why not?" says Hoppy.
"I cannot swim," says
the second little duckling.

Hoppy sees Bossy Bear.
"I am a duckling," says Bossy.
Hoppy thinks that this is very
funny.
"I will go to the duck pond
too," he says. "Duckling can
drive my car. This is
a very funny trick. Silly
Dilly Duck cannot see us."
The second little duckling
gets into Hoppy's car.

They all go along the lane.
Dilly Duck,
Bossy Bear,
Hoppy Rabbit
and one little duckling.
But Dilly Duck does not see
her very funny ducklings.

Soon they meet Paddy Dog.
Paddy Dog plays with his
little red scooter.
"Where are you going?"
says Paddy Dog.
"To the duck pond," says
the third little duckling.
"But I do not want to go."
"Why not?" says Paddy Dog.
"I cannot swim," says
the third little duckling.

Paddy Dog thinks that
this is very funny.
"Bossy and Hoppy are very
funny ducklings," he says.
"I will play a trick too.
Duckling can play with
my little red scooter.
I will be the third
little duckling. Silly
Dilly Duck will not see."

They all go along the lane.
Dilly Duck,
   Bossy Bear,
      Hoppy Rabbit
         and Paddy Dog.
But no little ducklings!
Ozzie Owl is in the old tree.
"Hoo-hoo-hoo!" he hoots.
Cuddly Cat jumps down from
the tree. She thinks they
are all very funny.

At last they come to the pond.
Flippy Frog and Merry Mole
are there. They say,
"What funny ducklings."
Then Dilly Duck sees them.
She is afraid. She looks all
round for her lost ducklings.
And here they come!
One on skates,
   one in the car,
      one on the scooter.

But the little ducklings go
too fast. They cannot stop!
SPLASH! SPLASH! SPLASH!
Three little ducklings
fall into the pond.
Bossy Bear, Hoppy Rabbit
and Paddy Dog are all afraid.
"What can we do?
The three little ducklings
cannot swim," they say.

"You are silly!" says
Dilly Duck.
"You must know that all little
ducklings can swim."
She hops into the pond too.
Off they go.
Dilly Duck goes first and the
three little ducklings swim
behind her. Silly Dilly Duck
is not so silly after all!

Say these words again

thinks	plays
afraid	roller-skates
first	drives
jumps	second
duckling	funny
swim	scooter
trick	third

What are they doing?

skating

falling

jumping

driving

swimming

PADDY DOG sees a GHOST

Paddy Dog is in his little house. It is a very windy day. Paddy looks out of the window. He sees the leaves falling off the trees.
"It is a good day for doing some washing," he says. Paddy Dog likes to be clean.

Paddy goes to get all his
dirty washing.
"My sheets are dirty," he says
"and my pillow case too."
Paddy takes the table cloth.
He takes his scarf and his
dirty socks. He puts all the
dirty things into the wash tub.

Then Paddy Dog fills the wash
tub with very hot water.
He puts in lots of soap powder
Then he rubs and he scrubs
until his things are clean.
Paddy goes outside to hang
the clean things on the line.
The wind is blowing hard.

"Now I will go and see Dilly
Duck," says Paddy Dog.
He goes to the duck pond.
Dilly is washing her three
little ducklings.
"It is a good day for doing
washing," says Paddy Dog.
"You are silly!" says Dilly.
"The wind is blowing too hard
Look! All your washing is
blowing away."

"Oh no!" says Paddy Dog. He runs down the lane after his washing. He finds his socks in the hedge. He finds his table cloth on a bush. Flippy Frog finds the scarf and pillow case. They are in the pond.

Poor Paddy Dog.
His washing is all dirty.
He cannot find his sheet.
It is not in the hedge.
It is not in the bush.
It is not by the duck pond.
Is it in the forest?

It is very dark in the forest.
Paddy Dog is afraid.
Something goes "Hoo-hoo-hoo!"
Paddy sees something white.
It is up in the tree.
"A ghost!" says Paddy Dog.
He is not very brave.
Paddy Dog runs away fast.

Paddy runs to Hoppy Rabbit's
house. Hoppy is outside,
washing his little car.
He rubs and he scrubs until
it is clean.
"There is a ghost in the
forest!" says Paddy.
"No," says Hoppy Rabbit.
"Yes," says Paddy. "It is up
in the tree."
"Let us tell Bossy Bear,"
says Hoppy Rabbit.

They run to Bossy Bear's
house. Bossy is outside,
washing the windows.
He rubs and he scrubs until
they are clean.
"There is a ghost in the
forest!" say Hoppy and Paddy
"No," says Bossy.
"Yes," say Hoppy and Paddy.
"It is up in the tree."
"Let us tell Dilly Duck,"
says Bossy.

Dilly and her ducklings are by the duck pond. Merry Mole and Flippy Frog are there too.
"There is a ghost in the forest!" say Paddy and Hoppy and Bossy.
"You are silly!" says Dilly.
"Come and see," says Paddy Dog.

So they all go to the forest.
They are afraid, but they
try to be brave.
Then they see something
white in the tree.
"Hoo-hoo-hoo!" it goes.
They all hear it.
"It is a ghost!" says Dilly.
They are not brave at all.
They run away.

Then Cuddly Cat comes by.
She sees something white.
"Hoo-hoo-hoo!" it goes.
"What is that?" says Cuddly.
"It is a ghost in the tree,"
says Paddy Dog.
"I will go and see," says
Cuddly Cat.
"Look out!" says Hoppy.
"The ghost will get you!"

But Cuddly is very brave.
She goes up in the tree.
She lifts up part of the sheet.
"Hoo-hoo-hoo!"
"Look!" says Cuddly Cat.
They all shout,
"We know you!"
It is not a ghost.
It is Ozzie Owl!

Say these words again

windy   clean
blowing   shout
washing   pillow
window   soap powder
outside   something

What can you see?

tub

window

ghost

car

tree

65

HAPPY
HOPPY RABBIT

It is Hoppy Rabbit's birthday.
He puts out all the things
for his birthday party.
He finds a cloth to put
on the table. He puts the
food on the table too. There
are lots of good things
to eat.

All Hoppy's friends come
to the party. Paddy Dog and
Bossy Bear come first.
"Happy Birthday, Hoppy!"
they say.
"Here is a present for you,"
says Paddy. He gives Hoppy
a big red ball.
"Thank you," says Hoppy,
"I like to play games with
a ball."

Bossy Bear has a present for
Hoppy too.
"Oh, look. It is a kite!"
says Hoppy.
"Look, here come Merry Mole
and Flippy Frog," says Bossy.
"Happy Birthday, Hoppy," they
say. Flippy gives Hoppy a big
bunch of flowers.
"I like flowers," says Hoppy.

Merry Mole has some carrots
for Hoppy.
"I like eating carrots,"
he says. "Thank you."
Then Cuddly Cat comes with
a big basket.
"Thank you," says Hoppy.
He puts all his presents
into the basket.

Here comes Dilly Duck with her three little ducklings. She has made a birthday cake for Hoppy.
The ducklings give him lots and lots of big balloons.
Hoppy is very happy with all his birthday presents.

"Time to eat!" says Hoppy.
They all go to the table
and they begin to eat.
They eat and they eat until
all the food is gone.
"I like birthdays," says
Hoppy. "Time to play some
games now."

They go outside to play with
the big red ball. Hoppy throws
it to Paddy. He throws it
high into the air. The others
try to catch it. They jump up
high, but no one can get the
ball. Then Cuddly Cat jumps
up on to the fence. Now she
can catch it.
"This is a very good game!"
says Cuddly.

The wind begins to blow.
"Good!" says Hoppy. "Now
I can play with my kite."
He gets the red and blue kite
and he begins to run. The
wind is blowing hard, and
the kite goes up in the air.
"Look at it fly!" says
Bossy Bear.

"Let me have a go," says Paddy.
The kite goes up in the air.
"Let me have a go," says Dilly.
She begins to run, but she does not see Flippy Frog.
BUMP!
She falls over poor Flippy.
Silly Dilly Duck!

Dilly lets go of the kite and it goes up into the air. "Oh no!" they all say. Hoppy, Paddy and Bossy jump up to catch it. But it is stuck high up in the tree. They cannot get it.

Poor Hoppy Rabbit.
He is not very happy now.
"Look!" says Bossy. "I can
get it for you."
Bossy gets up into the tree.
He gets the kite and he begins
to come down.

Then Bossy stops.
"Oh no!" he says.
"I am stuck!"
Bossy cannot get down.
"What can we do?" says Dilly.
"Look!" says Hoppy. He runs
to get all the balloons.
Then he gets the basket.
He ties the balloons to the
basket. Then he lets it go.

Up goes the basket!
It goes up into the tree.
"Get in, Bossy!" says Hoppy.
So Bossy gets into the basket
and it begins to come down.
Down and down it comes.
BUMP!
The basket is down,
Bossy is down,
and the kite is down too!
"What a happy birthday!"
says happy Hoppy Rabbit.

Say these words again

cloth	outside
friends	air
food	throws
eat	catch
first	jumps
present	wind
games	stuck